About the autho

CW00666704

C. M. Vassie appears unable
collection of tales is intende
of fiction or as a travellers'
Yorkshire coast, the old seaside town of Whitby.

Of the author little is known other than the possibly
unhelpful fact that they also penned the bewilderingly
successful contemporary gothic novel *SCRAVIR - While
Whitby Sleeps*, set in the same location.

*"Damnations, what perfidy is this from that insolent pup,
C. M. Vassie? First Scravir and now these irritatingly
entertaining short stories. Enough is enough."*
Bram Stoker

*"Devil! Wretch! Dost thou then so much as dare to challenge
my Captaincy with mutinous claims of Knowledge on
Whaling Matters? Quick, Ishmael! Pass me a Harpoon with
barbs sharp as the needle-sleet of the Icy Sea, that I may run
this scoundrel through and boil their bumptious blubber."*
Captain Ahab

Also by **C. M. Vassie**

SCRAVIR - While Whitby Sleeps

The Moon Pool Trilogy
Moon Pool
We are POD

Making Plans for Michael

www.injinipress.co.uk

C.M.VASSIE

THE
Whale
Bone
Archers

and other
tall stories
of Whitby

injini press

Copyright © C. M. Vassie 2022

Illustrations and Map: C. M .Vassie

A catalogue record for this book is available from the British Library

ISBN: 978-0-9552437-7-6

Contents

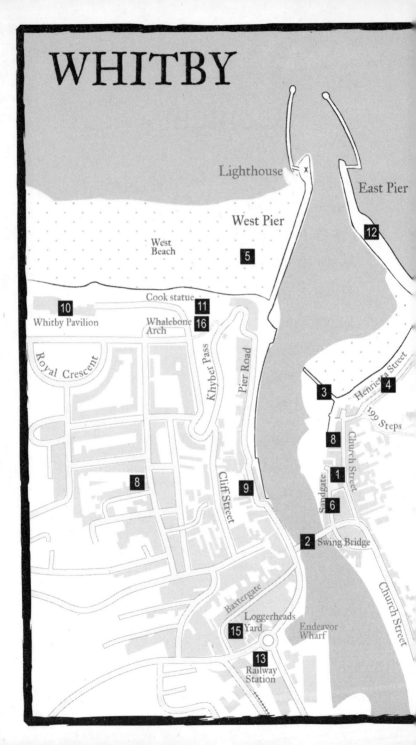

NORTH SEA

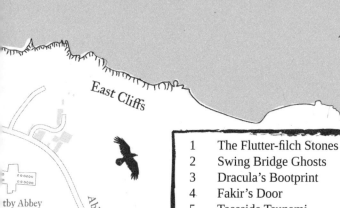

East Cliffs

...tby Abbey

Abbey Lane

Green Lane

Foreward

Much of what is written in this visitors' guide to Whitby is clearly nonsense. On the other hand, much of it is rooted in facts.

All of it is inspired by the author's deep love of Whitby. History is packed with unique places, artefacts and incidents that tell us about who and what we have been. The *Whale Bone Archers* tales aim to give a new slant on Whitby's intriguing past.

These tall stories - some amusing, others ghostly, all intense - are intended to provide an alternative way of exploring the fabric of the town and the lives of those who have lived here. The map will help readers pinpoint the exact spot where something did or did not happen.

At the back of the book, the *Endnotes* are waiting to spill the beans and give the reader a clear(ish) sense of exactly how little is true in each of the stories.

The author wishes to thank Whitby's wonderful independent bookshops for their support and helpful suggestions during the writing of this book. Special thanks to Fiona, Chris, Angela, Louise, and Peter.

The Flutter-filch Stones

In late November 1783, fresh from a successful venture that had earned each of them a small fortune from the sale of whale parts – bones for corset stays and umbrella rods, and blubber oil for lamps and candles - Messrs Nathaniel Wilde and George Sutcliffe met in the White Horse and Griffin on Church Street for an evening of gambling and carousing.

Both men arrived with heavy money pouches; each secretly determined to teach the other a damn good lesson in what they called the 'noble art of flutter-filching' (or *cheating* as the rest of us call it).

Wilde's normal weapon of choice was Whist, while Sutcliffe had previously declared himself enamoured of Faro, a card game he played at the guinea tables in Mayfair, but, in keeping with the occasion, they had agreed to play Hazard, a game requiring not cards but dice.

Upon seating himself at the bar, Mr Sutcliffe produced a unique set of dice carved and whittled from Icelandic walrus tusks. He claimed that the dice had arrived earlier that year on a whaler called the *Misanthrope* that had sailed from Reykjavik laden with pilot whales and puffins. Since the good folk of Whitby had shown scant interest in eating either pilot whales or puffins, the crew of the *Misanthrope* had been reduced to selling their possessions in order to raise the funds to buy vitals and rum for their journey home. And so it was that the Icelandic walrus dice had ended in Mr Sutcliffe's ownership.

Mr Wilde was not to be outdone. He too had brought a set of dice. These were slightly larger than Mr Sutcliffe's and were yellower in hue, with cream-coloured dots upon their surfaces. Mr Wilde averred that his dice were fashioned from polar bear bone inlaid with elephant ivory. When challenged as to how the maker of such dice could have had access to exotic materials that originated on two different continents, Wilde explained that the items had been fashioned for King Henry III in 1256 following the death of the elephant given to him by the King of France the previous year. Both polar bear and elephant had been installed at the Tower of London for the king's pleasure but had died in an unfortunate incident involving a yeoman and a halibut.

There being much at stake Mr Wilde asked that the landlord of the White Horse and Griffin, a Jonathan Pannett, be prevailed upon to assess all the dice and confirm that neither set had been tampered with. The landlord was happy to oblige; as a publican he had seen more than his share of fights and brawls resulting from flutter-filching, and the nefarious use of loaded dice known as spot loaders, floppers, cappers and missouts.

Mr Pannett having declared himself satisfied with both sets of dice, the toss of a coin, called by Mr Pannett, determined that Mr Wilde's dice would be used for the contest.

Phineas Stephenson, chief actuary at the prestigious Whitby firm of Cook, Stephenson and Stew was entrusted with tabulating the contest and handling the monies using his own proven and excruciatingly dull method of quintuple entry book-keeping.

The game of Hazard continued into the small hours as the money changed hands, back and forth, this way and that. A crowd gathered at the windows to watch the proceedings, drinking copiously and shouting and cheering each change of fortune. By midnight the publican declared the cellars dry as every last barrel on the premises had been emptied. Denied further liquid refreshment, the vast majority of the onlookers staggered home, but still Sutcliffe and Wilde tossed the dice, each trying to bankrupt the other.

The first whisper of the rising sun was caressing the waves when finally Mr Wilde had the better of Mr Sutcliffe, leaving him out of pocket and pouch to the tune of some two hundred and fourteen guineas. A triumphant Mr Wilde promptly commissioned the local hatter, who had stayed to the very end of the contest, to make him a special top hat one yard in height to celebrate his success.

In his haste, his pouch heaving with his winnings, Mr Wilde left the White Horse & Griffin in such a state of elation that he left his dice at the bar. Meanwhile the disconsolate Mr Sutcliffe tramped to his lodgings having squandered a small fortune.

And so events might have drawn to a close had not Phineas Stephenson, the actuary, noticed the discarded dice and taken advantage of the opportunity to verify their honesty for himself. This he did by floating the dice in the last of his ale whereupon he observed that the dice kept turning to leave the four spot or one spot sides facing upwards. His suspicions aroused, he looked about and spotted a third dice on the floor beneath the chair upon which Mr Wilde had been sitting. This third dice, which looked identical to the two that had been used in the game, was dropped into a second glass and repeatedly turned until the two spot faced upwards.

The following morning Phineas Stephenson found a barmaid willing to testify that Mr Wilde had met with the publican, Jonathan Pannett, over luncheon the previous day, hours before the contest, though she could not say what the two men had discussed. She also averred that Pannett had in his possession various double-headed coins.

As everyone knows, in Hazard a two spot will cost the caster his turn. Mr Stephenson therefore surmised that Mr Wilde had been switching dice, keeping the dice loaded toward the four spot for himself and giving the dice loaded towards the two spot to his opponent.

Accompanied by a constable and the town's watchman, Mr Stephenson confronted Mr Wilde who, fearing imprisonment, confessed to his crime. To avoid disgrace Mr Wilde not only returned Mr Sutcliffe his money but also agreed to donate one hundred and fifty guineas to Nathaniel Cholmley as a contribution towards the construction of the town hall about to be erected on Church Street. It was further agreed that three stones on the corner of the northern elevation of the old town hall, seven stone rows up, would be marked with the loaded spots that had given the despicable Mr Wilde his unfair advantage. A humiliated Mr Wilde left the town the following day, never to return.

The three Flutter-filch stones – four spots, two spots, and one spot - have sat side by side on the old town hall ever since.

Swing Bridge Ghosts

When Mabel Theresa Duncombe officially opened the new Whitby swing bridge in July 1909 she could scarcely have imagined the impact the new crossing would have, not only on the living but also on the dead.

Since 1351 tolls had been collected at what was then a wooden bridge over the Esk, and the new bridge of 1909 was not the first opening bridge to connect the two sides of the town, the first swing bridge having opened in 1833. But the new bridge was the first to greet the arrival of the motor car.

In March 1910 the first Yorkshire car, a Jowett 6.4 HP light car with a 816cc flat twin water-cooled engine, arrived in Whitby, paid the toll and crossed the Esk from west to east, to the amazement of the local population. There were some 700 cars on the roads of England in 1900 but none had ventured as far as Whitby. It was a great occasion.

The driver of the car was Charles Copperthwaite, inventor of the spring-loaded hunting boot, a device that enabled the wearer to 'bag more grouse than a Leaping Lord'. In the car with him was his wife Bromelia.

They parked outside the newly built Customs House Hotel on Bridge Street, now known as the Dolphin Hotel, where they met the magnet magnate Fred Flowers and his fiancé Gertrude Quince Lugs, who had travelled to Whitby by train. The two couples had what one of the waitresses called 'the largest meal I ever did serve' as the party declared that they wished to eat everything on the menu, accompanied by all the ales and wines the hotel had to offer. It was said that, in his cups, Fred Flowers had even tried to eat the menu itself.

Towards midnight the party had eaten their fill, smoked more cigars and drunk more port than any mortal soul before or since.

Following the somewhat tetchy transport-related disagreement that had occurred during the twelfth course of devilled crab, Copperthwaite decided it was time to prove to Flowers that the age of the motor car had arrived and he therefore declared that he would drive them both to Sandsend and 'put the car through its paces'.

The hotel manager, Bram Eskerby, sought in vain to persuade the party to wait until morning and later told the Whitby Gazette that all four were 'somewhat the worse for wear'.

Copperthwaite and Flowers were adamant. While their lady folk staggered up to the bedrooms, the two men donned leather helmets and goggles, climbed into the car and set off across the swing bridge.

They did not even make it to the other side. Eyewitnesses testified that the car, having veered wildly from side to side, stopped just past the middle of the bridge. The men were heard laughing then singing. Presently, insults were thrown back and forth. A window on the second floor of the hotel flew open and Bromelia was heard shouting into the night, begging her husband to reverse back across the bridge to the hotel so that they might all get a good night's sleep.

'Bugger that for a game of soldiers, Bromelia! We will sleep it off right here,' Copperthwaite replied at the top of his voice. 'Look at the view, woman!'

A short time later the window was closed, the two men were asleep and quiet returned to the harbour, the only sounds being the gentle lapping of water and the clicking of the rigging against the masts of the boats.

At five in the morning, shortly before dawn, the first ship appeared in the harbour with the rising tide and the bridge operator, roused from his slumbers in the bridge house, put the motors into gear. The two sides of the bridge began to rotate and the road sections swung round ninety degrees to create the channel through which the tall ship might pass into the safety of the upper harbour.

It was precisely at the moment the ship was passing through the open bridge that Charles Copperthwaite woke from his drunken slumbers. On seeing a vessel passing within a few metres of his face, confused as to his situation and groggily concluding that his eyes were playing tricks on him, Copperthwaite became alarmed. He lurched out of the car, cranked the starter handle and fired up the engine, clambered back into the vehicle and raced forwards along the road towards what he imagined must be safety.

Since the bridge was open, the car barely covered twenty metres before driving off the end of the road and plunging into the icy waters. Blind drunk and stuck in the dark in a car at the bottom of the harbour, the two men died before they could be saved.

It is said that on March mornings when the bridge is opened before daybreak, you can sometimes see a ghostly Jowett 6.4 HP light car with a 816cc flat twin water-cooled engine suddenly appear, only to speed across the short stretch of road and fly off the end into the water, accompanied by muffled cries and a deep male voice shouting:

'Bugger that for a game of soldiers, Bromelia.'

Dracula's Bootprint

It is often believed that Stoker's tale of Dracula is simply the product of a fevered imagination, a work of fiction, if you will. But to believe that is to over-look the evidence before our very eyes.

Stroll to the ancient Tate Hill Pier and you will discover one of the town's best kept secrets; the imprint of Count Dracula's boot.

Originally known as East Pier and then Burgess Pier, the Tate Hill Pier has witnessed the comings and goings of hundreds of collier ships that would unload their cargos of coal before venturing back out onto the North Sea.

As many will know, it was on Tate Hill Sands, beside this very pier, that Bram Stoker told us the

Russian vessel Demeter of Varna ran aground in a storm in 1887. A large dog was seen to leap from the wreck and disappear up the 199 steps towards the abbey.

The captain of the Demeter had been found dead on the broken deck of his vessel, fastened by his hands to a spoke of the wheel. The good folk of Whitby, being seafarers themselves and understanding only too well the vagaries of a cruel sea, decided the captain deserved a proper burial. A hundred boats crammed the harbour as a group of Whitby's finest captains carried the coffin from Tate Hill Pier up the steps to the churchyard.

At the precise moment that the coffin reached the churchyard at the top of the hill a young local girl, Lucy Swales, reported that she saw 'a tall gentleman of very pale complexion' emerge from between the houses and step down onto Tate Hill Pier to approach the wreck of the Demeter.

In the wake of the storm that had thrown the vessel into the harbour and smashed her onto Tate Hill Sands, urgent repairs had been carried out to strengthen the pier. Lucy Swales swore that the tall gentleman was responsible for the deep impression of a left boot that appeared in the wet concrete that day. She further declared that he had appeared of mournful complexion and had repeatedly clenched his fists as he looked down upon the wreck before he 'turned and looked at me in a manner that made my blood run cold'.

The girl's words were dismissed as the confabulations of a child but, over one hundred and thirty years later, the size twelve bootprint is still there on Tate Hill Pier.

In all that time the bootprint has shown no sign of aging and remains as crisp as the day it was made. Some locals leaving the nearby hostelry at closing time have reported the bootprint leering malevolently towards them 'as if possessed of dark forces'.

Perhaps most curious of all, several fishermen have contended, over the decades, that even during heaviest downpours the bootprint never collects water. As mariner John Sweard observed in 1937, 'It is as if the rain, like the seas that tossed the Demeter onto the sands, wants nothing to do with the evil that bootprint represents.'

Fakir's Door

Being the curious tale of Cornelius Bean and the fakir's door.

On 24th September 1599 a group of Londoners met to petition Queen Elizabeth I to set up a company to "to venter in a voiage to ye Est Indies".

And so began 350 years of British presence in India. Much has been written of the good and bad things that happened during a period that culminates with the creation of the British Raj in 1858.

How many of us think of India when we wander up Henrietta Street to gaze down at the harbour or to purchase a brace of kippers from Fortune's smokehouse?

And yet, the door of 37 Henrietta Street provides a fascinating link to that exotic world almost five thousand miles to the east. To gaze upon that door is to glimpse the timeless magic of the fakir's bed of nails for that is indeed where this amazing artefact originated.

It was, of course, standard practice that a true 'bed of nails' should include 680 nails arranged in forty rows of seventeen nails. Reference to this is found in the Mahabharata, an epic Sanskrit poem of ancient India, written around 300BC. Those of keen eye will immediately confirm that there are forty rows of nails upon the door and that each row contains (or once contained) seventeen nails.

To the early British explorers, the bed of nails must be a form of punishment rather than a spiritual expression of mysticism. It was curiosity that persuaded Cornelius Bean, mariner, to purchase a bed of nails from a fakir who lived in a side street beside the Mahatma Jyotiba Phule Market in Bombay, now called Mumbai.

The item took over a year to complete the journey from Mumbai to Whitby, travelling overland along the old silk road through the Middle East and Europe. Cornelius Bean meanwhile served as a crewman on the *Escutcheon*, a vessel that rounded the Cape of Good Hope in storms so violent as to leave Mr Bean 'in fear for my very life'.

Upon arrival back in Whitby, Mr Bean assured his wife that his days of circumnavigating the globe were over and that he had it in mind henceforth to earn a living by touring with the circus and lying on his bed of nails. His wife Alice was horrified, worried that either the family would become a laughing stock or her husband would puncture himself and bleed to death, or both. She insisted that he abandon his 'foolishness' and instead use the bed of nails to replace the front door which, in truth, had been falling apart for some time. Faced with his wife's wrath, Cornelius succumbed.

The nails were smashed and blunted, and holes cut to accommodate the door furniture: two letterboxes (one for him and one for the rest of the family, as was the custom at that time), a door handle and various locks.

Providence ensured that, after all the adjustments had been made, it was discovered that precisely 37 nails had been sacrificed in the conversion of the bed into a door, leaving just 643 nails upon the door. As 37 was also the number of the house, it was considered by all parties a sign of good fortune, and the couple agreed to speak no more about the incident.

Alice continued her employment as a pincushion upholsterer. Cornelius, having failed to earn a living performing increasingly pathetic stunts involving coloured buckets and picking up rows of live crabs with his mouth on the West Pier, sadly, finished his days rolling around on limpet-covered rocks at Kettleness in futile attempts to sooth his aching back.

Teesside Tsunami

On certain days as you stand on the West Pier at high tide looking out along the beach, particularly on those days when a sea mist hangs heavily and Sandsend appears to disappear altogether, you will notice strange movement across the surface of the water. As if two ducks with their butts in the air were making their way forwards together over the submerged sand, away from the pier, while the waves sweep in and out. And maybe other pairs of ducks, also heads down, following alongside. But not quite ducks, because they are too thin and maybe a little too pointy. Depending on the light the objects may seem grey or grey-brown and even, on occasions, appear almost hairy.

From time to time the objects will appear to turn and come towards you, at the same "easy Sunday morning" pace. It doesn't matter how hard the waves rush the beach or how much sea foam is tumbling towards the shore. Nothing deflects their course as these pairs of objects amble forward or head away without a care in the world.

Most of us give up after a few minutes and decide that some things are simply not meant to be understood; as unfathomable as the force that drives socks to all end up hiding inside the quilt cover when you put them in the washing machine.

To find the cause of our strange phenomenon we have to cross to the other side of the harbour and step back hundred and twenty years or so.

Beside the famous 199 steps is a very steep road and its name gives us a clue as to what is happening on the beach. For years Whitby locals descended Donkey Road with their animals, taking them from Abbey Field down and through the town to the west beach where they gave rides to day-trippers. Sepia photographs show us families – everyone in hats, the women in long dresses, the men in dark suits – gathered round a donkey on which perches a small child clinging to the saddle uncertain whether to shriek with joy or burst into tears.

It was called the Teesside Tsunami by some, though it ran from Redcar to Robin Hood's Bay. Others denied that anything had ever occurred that fateful day in 1906 when everything on the beach was swept away in the space of a couple of minutes.

The epicentre was Whitby.

The afternoon had arrived gently enough. The kittiwakes, having flown up from their favourite cliffs in Scarborough, filled the clear air with their cries. A large pod of dolphins had been seen from the pier mid-morning, causing great excitement. The sun shone brightly in a blue sky and everyone from holidaymaker to street urchin, lobsterman and Whitby jet carver was outside enjoying a perfect summer's day as the waves whispered up and down the sands.

The donkey rides were busy that day. Toffee, Charley, Snowdrop and Mo had been carrying children back and forth since 11am when the falling tide had exposed enough of the sand to get started. The donkeys had barely had a moment to stop and stare at the shimmering sea.

Further along the sands, the beach huts with their gaudily painted doors were all open. Buckets and spades were strewn about. Castles rose and fell. Crabs crouched and hid. Seaweed sweated it out upon the sprawling rocks, awaiting the return of the cool sea.

All was well with the world.

And then, out of nowhere, came a shriek as a woman noticed a wave that was somehow wrong. Too high and too wide. In a fraction of a second she had grabbed her son, kicking over his sandcastle, and was racing bare foot along the beach towards the slipway that led up to Battery Parade as fast as her legs would carry her.

Across the beach, people looked up to see the cause of the commotion. There was something about the colour of the wave that seemed ominous, a turquoise translucence that set it apart from the sea. Panic spread rapidly as people left their belongings and ran. Gull cries were drowned by human shouts. Children were plucked off donkeys' backs, dresses were hoisted to the point of shin showing indecency, hats flew off heads and people rushed pell-mell across the sands, desperate to escape the beach.

The threat grew second by second. It was now obvious that this was no ordinary wave. By the time it reached the harbour jaws, it delivered a huge smack of water that exploded so high as to drown the beacon altogether for an instant. The roar of the water as it flew through the legs of the piers caused grown men to shout for their mothers. And still the wave kept coming, now over four metres high.

By the lighthouse people clung for dear life to the railings as their feet were swept away from under them. A small dog snatched by the surging swell disappeared off the pier into the sea, where it yelped a couple of times then was gone.

And still people ran as if their lives depended on it. Up on the cliff by the Whale Bone Arch, families picnicking on the grass stood up to stare in horror at the scene below. Babies sensing their parents' unhappiness began to cry.

In the chaos and confusion everyone forgot Toffee, Charley, Snowdrop and Mo, still bearing their saddles and reins, waiting patiently for somebody to decide where they must go. Their owners had run from danger along with everyone else. Getting a donkey to run was simply not an option and so they had been left standing on the sands as the wall of water flung itself towards the cliffs.

A boy standing by the lookout post at the end of Battery Parade spotted the donkeys in the seconds before the wave struck but, in his shock, he could not utter a sound.

And then it was too late.

The wave thrashed the cliff so hard that those up

by the Whale Bone Arch swore they felt the cliff move. A haberdasher from Ripon who had come to Whitby to help her lumbago said she heard a donkey begin to bray, a "awful plaintiff cry" that had been swallowed up in the raging noise of the sea.

A couple of seconds later it was all done. The wave retreated back whence it had come, taking everything with it; buckets and spades, hats and sandwiches, walking sticks and parasols, chairs and shoes …

… and four donkeys.

The perfect day blinked back as if it had never gone. The sun shone brightly in an azure blue sky and the sea acted is if nothing had happened.

And that is why on those days when a sea mist hangs heavy obscuring the view of Sandsend in the distance, you may notice four pairs of ears moving to and fro across the waves. Beneath the surface, four lost donkeys are walking slowly along the beach waiting to take children for a ride.

Captains' Hooks

Silas Waymans was used to people reaching out and touching his collar, after all touching a sailor's collar brought good luck and there was never a shortage of townsfolk in need of good luck, particularly after the landslide in 1786 that had destroyed so many homes on Henrietta Street.

Life was hard; that winter had been particularly harsh and spring still felt as far away as a harvest moon. So, as Silas began preparations for his next voyage to the ice waters around Greenland in search of whales, his thoughts turned to what he might do to protect his ship and crew.

All the ships' captains, and their crews, were superstitious men. The sea was dangerous and rough and no one wished to tempt fate by using words that must not be spoken or taking on board items that must be left on land. There was no place for land animals or flowers or, most of all, the banana, a fruit that brought nothing but bad luck wherever it went.

Silas had never seen a banana himself, but he had heard about them and knew the destruction they had brought to mariners foolish enough to take them on board. When he was setting sail to the Greenland Sea, where icebergs creaked and leviathans lurked, a captain must be master of his fate, guardian of his soul, protector of his crew, and not the hapless architect of his own misfortune.

Any sailor who used the word pig or cat or hare or rabbit would be dropped off at the nearest port and left to find his own passage back to Whitby or, if no port could be reached, thrown overboard. For those who must refer to forbidden animals there was a whole range of circumlocutions to protect the crew and the ship. A sailor desperate to talk about swine could refer to the long-nosed fellow, the rabbit was a mappie, and a hare was a loppy lugs.

Let landlubbers scoff, their soft pampered lives knew nothing of the dangers faced at sea.

So it was that Silas met with eight other captains on a damp evening in early March when the mist wrapped its tendrils around the masts of the ships, and cold clung to the chimney pots. They sat down in the White Horse Inn, that would one day become the Black Horse Inn, on Church Street. The stage-coach to York had just left and the bar was empty. Each man having had his fill of snuff and ale, talk turned to the voyages on which they would soon embark.

'Misfortune hangs around our necks like Aipaloovik's Anchor,' said Silas, stroking his thick beard. 'We must turn the tide in our favour, gentle-men, or run the gauntlet. Any thoughts?'

'I've forty crew, Silas,' said Thomas Banks, captain of the Valiant. 'Assembling a full comple-ment without enlisting a single lunkhead is a devil's job. I've lost count of the times I have had a man flogged for turning us about widdershins instead of sungates.'

'We must maximise our good luck here at home,' suggested Thelonius Baxter, captain of the Four Sisters. 'Counterbalance the forces of misfortune with actions that protect us from the perils of the deep.'

'My thoughts exactly,' agreed Silas. 'Here is my plan.'

And so it was that the captains agreed that night

to position a set of hooks on the west side wall in Sandgate, upon which they would each hang one of their shirts the day they left port. Beside the shirts a notice was fixed, inviting friends, family and well-wishers to touch the collars of the shirts as they went about their business, to bring good luck to the crews and families of those at sea.

By the end of March all ships had sailed. Through the summer and early autumn, the shirts hung on the wall in all weathers. Wives and sisters, mothers and brothers and children would reach out and touch the collars and remember their loved ones at sea and hope and pray that all was well. Storms came and went. New babes were born. Summer heat brought strawberries and lazy days. Then autumn came in a tumble of apples and slippery stones.

And finally, a boy fishing for cod and coalfish at the end of the harbour jaws spotted the masts rising on the horizon and raced to find his mother. Within a week all nine ships had returned safely. Not a single ship was lost that year among those whose captains that had hung a shirt.

The hooks became known as the Captains' Hooks. Legend has it that J.M.Barrie was so inspired by this tale that he called one of his famous characters after the Captains' Hooks. Is it true, who knows?

To those cynics who see the hooks and say "why do these hooks appear so modern?" or "how could they possibly bear the collars of whaling captains who died two hundred and forty years ago?" we must reply that the sea, like Whitby itself, is a very mysterious place.

Phantom Chippy

Whitby has many fish and chip shops, around forty of them, but there is one that you would have to be very very lucky to see.

There is just a chance, if you wander the streets of the harbour or the old town after midnight, that you will catch a glimpse of the phantom fish and chip shop of Whitby.

The Nuclear Fishun chippy opened its doors on Pier Road in September 1956 and was a celebration of the modern world that was emerging after the Second World War. Just two years earlier the Borax-III nuclear power plant, the planet's first functioning nuclear power station, had been powered up close to the small town of Arco in Idaho and Fred Hazeley, the proud owner of Whitby's newest chippy was keen to ensure that event did not pass unnoticed.

On opening night it is fair to say that patrons were dazzled by their new eatery. Beneath the illuminated menu board, a spanking new AMI I 200 Vinyl juke-box, with selector wheel and spearmint trim modelled on the 3.7 litre Plymouth Fury, played all the latest hits: Doris Day, Elvis Presley, Bill Haley & His Comets, Lonnie Donegan, The Chordettes, Fats Domino, and more.

There was the triple frying station with its gleaming chrome finish and, hanging from the ceiling, the front grill of an American pink and brown 5 litre Mercury Montclair automobile, complete with working headlamps.

And, icing on the fishcake, there was the huge magical blue and red neon sign that beamed the words *Nuclear Fishun Chips* so brightly that it could be seen from across the harbour at the top of Abbey Steps.

The town's newly invented *teenagers* were in awe of the new establishment and in the space of a couple of days abandoned every other chippy in town. Girls in white bobby socks, plaid pleated skirts and Peter Pan collar blouses; and lads in black trousers, loafers, bright shirts and a generous dollop of

Brylcreem or Vaseline slopping about in their hair, crowded into the Nuclear Fishun chippy and twisted the night away while their chips turned golden in the fryers.

'It were like Whitby had morphed into Las Vegas,' recalls Eddie Dunn. 'Sheer bloody magic!'

'It wiped silly smiles off their smug faces in Scarborough,' agrees Edith Smurthwaite.

Not everyone was happy. Councillor Grumpthorpe complained that the new chippy 'looked like a bloody Christmas Tree'. He urged the council to close the establishment to 'save our young people from temptation and debauchery'.

The Whitby Gazette reported Grumpthorpe's special displeasure at the availability of free condiments, claiming that these encouraged patrons to over-excite their taste buds in a manner that was positively indecent.

The Yorkshire Post carried a snide article written by Scarborough's Mayor, Eric Fordham, complaining that Whitby's gaudy cafés and chippies 'lowered the tone' of the region.

The scene was set for a battle royal.

While in France and Belgium they slugged it out as to which nation had invented chips, in the 17th or 18th century, in Whitby scuffles broke out as to whether a traditional food must be served in a traditional way or allowed 'to fall into the wrong hands.'

It wasn't the first time that fish and chips had brought altercations to Whitby. Since the first fish and chip shop had opened its doors in 1928 the town had struggled to adjust. Within two years fish & chips had become so popular that every second building in the town centre had been transformed into a fish and chip shop. Preferring fried food to anything else on God's earth, the economy was turned on its head. Banks and building societies closed as people preferred fries and batter to coins and banknotes and, because the new currency was perishable, entrepreneurs like Samuel Thwing created his new Chippidaire refrigeration system to help Whitby folk freeze and protect their savings. The most successful of these northern enterprises became known as *blue chip companies*.

At the height of the Great Chip Rush in 1931 even Whitby's casinos switched from coins and counters to the new currency, from which the phrase 'when the chips are down' first entered the English language. The green baize on poker and roulette tables was replaced with waxed cloth that could be wiped down at the end of the evening to remove the congealed beef dripping.

So many colourful phrases, such as 'a chip off the old block', 'she's got a chip on her shoulder' and 'he's had his chips', date back to this period of fish and chip excess.

By 1956 things had calmed down but there were still Whitby residents who remembered the trauma of 1931 so Grumpthorpe's complaints did not fall on deaf ears.

In the early hours on Sunday morning on 9th December 1956 the town was woken up by a massive explosion. Curtains were flung open on Henrietta Street. Across the harbour *Nuclear Fishun Chips* was in flames, its neon sign in pieces on the road, vinyl records from the AMI I 200 jukebox scattered across the pavement, the Mercury Montclair's front bumper hanging from a lamp post.

A fisherman loading lobster pots in the harbour testified that, before the fire engines arrived, he saw the owner race down the street towards his burning business.

'Hazeley stood there silhouetted against the flaming inferno, shouting oaths into the night,' recalled Dennis Crabbe. 'Terrible curses. He swore the whole town would pay for the arson attack. Said we would be cursed forever and would never forget him then, pulling the front bumper of the Mercury Montclair automobile from the lamppost, he ran away towards Khyber Pass.'

They never did establish the identity of the arsonists. Many in the town thought Grumpthwaite and his circle of temperance activists the ringleaders. Others blamed the chippies, in Whitby or even as far away as Scarborough, saying that they had acted out of jealousy or to protect their businesses from the dazzling entrepreneurial skills of Fred Hazeley.

Hazeley has never been seen again but his curse remains to this day.

Even now the ghostly echo of the *Nuclear Fishun Chips* pops up randomly across the town, usually after midnight.

One minute a street is sleeping quietly, the next minute one of the shop frontages has suddenly transformed into a 1950's fish and chip shop. Rock & Roll blares from an AMI I 200 jukebox with selector wheel and spearmint trim, the sweet smell of fish and chips hangs heavy in the air. The sound of youngsters laughing and twisting mingles with sound of orders being called out on a ghostly Tannoy system.

'Number 43, one of each twice with bits and two Bubble Up sodas.'

'Number 47, two large chips and complimentary ketchup.'

After a few minutes a huge explosion rattles the windows, and silence and darkness return.

The generation that torched the chippy are long gone but some of the youngsters who pressed the jukebox buttons are still alive.

'I miss it,' says 82-year-old Edith Smurthwaite, who still lives above a shop in the town centre. 'For us it were magic. It were a terrible thing those old farts did to my generation.'

'I keep my windows open at night, all year, and whenever I hear Fats Domino or Bill Haley out in the street I grab my bobby socks and my pleated skirt, pull them on and head outside.' Edith gazes fondly into her memories. 'I'm not as fleet on my pegs as I were, unfortunately. One night it were right there, on Skinner Street. Those wonderful red and blue neon lights lit the shop fronts like Christmas and Doris Day were singing *Whatever Will Be, Will Be*.'

'I were just three shops away when the whole thing blew up and vanished into the night, but I keep the memory alive right here.' She pats her chest and smiles fondly. 'What I'd give for a Bubble Up soda at Nuclear Fishun Chips.'

The Smug Smugglers of Arguments Yard

'They have just been spotted on Church Street, heading into Arguments Yard!' Robert announces, still panting from his exertions.

Customs Officer Captain Harold Hutchinson smiles and reaches for his weapons. 'Then we will intercept them and bring them to book,' he tells his apprentice. 'Fetch Tom.'

'He is asleep, Sir.'

'Kick the lazy loafer out of bed. We leave in two minutes.'

It is close to midnight and pouring with cold November rain as Harold Hutchinson emerges from his fine house on Skinner Street with his two young apprentices at his side. They hurry down Flowergate towards the Golden Lion pub, from which it is a few short steps to the bridge that will take them over the River Esk and into the old town.

Rounding the corner onto St Ann's Staith, Hutchinson slips and tumbles headlong into a rancid wall of whale blubber. His men prise him out of the fat and set him on his feet, sniggering helplessly at the state of him.

'What the devil, is this?' Hutchinson explodes.

'It's blubber, Mr Hutchinson. From the *Four Sisters,*' Robert explains.

'She returned from Greenland this afternoon,' Tom adds.

'I know it's blubber, you oafs! I mean why is it here?'

The apprentices shrug their shoulders.

'Well, don't stand there gawping, miserable runts,' Hutchinson bellows. 'Get after those bastard smugglers or I'll have you in irons! And when I find whoever is responsible for this disgusting disgrace on the highway I will have him flogged.'

With gelatinous gobbets of blubber clinging to his clothes and stinking from head to toe, Hutchinson staggers across the stone bridge after his men, praying they are not too late.

It is the third time in a week that he has received

intelligence that the smugglers are busy on Church Street and he prays that this time he will finally catch the scoundrels red-handed. Entering Sandgate he passes two women in voluminous coats, coming in the opposite direction. He recognises one of them, a foul-mouthed lass, Beth, the wife of one of the laggards that the Navy press-ganged in September.

'Out of my way, slatterns' he shouts.

'He should know,' Beth says to the other woman. 'His own house is a bordello. Holy Hutchinson? Whoremonger Harold, more like.'

'He'll have a bath if he knows what's good for him,' suggests the second woman. 'We can smell you halfway down the street, love.'

Hutchinson ignores the women's laughter as he passes the Captains' Hooks on his way to Market Square.

Some 6000 gallons of rum, brandy and Geneva were intercepted on a ship bound for Whitby just two weeks ago, not far from Sandsend but Hutchinson has received intelligence that another ship avoided the law two nights ago and reached the shore. He is determined to seize the goods and apprehend the smugglers.

Part of the problem for all those trying to impose the rule of law in the old town is the lattice of secret passages, snickets, yards and ginnels that run between the buildings. A smuggler can be in fingertip reach then abruptly disappear into the lacklight down a narrow alley. Goods may be passed from window to window above the ground or carried out of sight along underground tunnels.

Suddenly, Hutchinson stops and smacks his forehead with the palm of his hand. The women. They are probably in on the act; smuggling contraband beneath their skirts and coats. Thinking about it, Beth was a much thinner woman the last time he set eyes on her. No doubt the pair of them are carrying bladders of rum and brandy hanging from belts beneath their skirts. He curses, torn between the desire to reach Arguments Yard and the urge to turn tail and chase after the women.

By the time he reaches the entrance to the yard, Hutchinson is soaking wet from the rain, sweating profusely and gagging from the noisome stench of the melting blubber. He is steaming. He rests for a moment, leaning against the wall of the ginnel to catch his breath. Up ahead are the shouts of a fight in full swing. Punches are being thrown.

'Leave my man alone, you twisted lump of spittle-spume!' screams a woman's voice.

A thwacking sound is followed by a yelp of pain.

Hutchinson unsheathes his sword and steps into the yard to defend his lads.

It is an unfair contest, the two boys are surrounded by three grown men and three women. Robert is slugging it out with two of the fishermen while a dog barks and snaps at Tom's heels. The third man has pinned Tom's arms behind his back and two women beat Tom across the head with planks of wood.

It is too dark to identify the assailants.

'Unhand my lads or feel my blade,' Hutchinson shouts, swinging his sword wildly in the air at the top of the steps.

The women and two of the men retreat, cursing. Tom jumps forwards clutching his head. The third man, a balding burly rock of muscle and fists, turns to sneer at Hutchinson.

'You think I fear your dandy blade, you limpet?' he says, throwing a hefty punch into Robert's belly. 'I've met turbot tougher than thee.'

Robert crumples and, as he falls, Hutchinson catches sight of a row of kegs by the wall just up from the steps that lead down to the water's edge.

The customs officer knows when he has met his match and he can hear from the man's voice that he is not a local. A Geordie from up the coast, most likely.

'Come, gentlemen,' Hutchinson says, his sword still raised. 'What say we strike a deal? Something for everyone? How many kegs have you? Those five and what else?'

The three men and the three women exchange glances. At the end of the day, a deal will buy them time to get their goods up Donkey Road and out of Whitby before dawn. Profits before prison.

'There's what you see,' says the smallest of the women, who has the broad shoulders of someone used to hauling heavy boxes. 'Take one keg and let us be.'

Hutchinson makes a show of considering the offer. He knows she is lying but, with Robert unconscious on the ground and Tom clutching his head, they are outnumbered. Even with his sword, he will probably receive a beating if he insists on a fight.

'Two kegs. Two kegs and we'll talk no more. Tom, get that useless scrimp on his feet. You'll carry a keg between you then return for the second.' Hutchinson turns to the smugglers and nods. 'Taxes duly paid and accepted. Gentlemen. Ladies.'

The customs party are heading back up the passage towards Church Street when a voice rings out.

'Smells worse than a dead man's kecks, that one.

There's reet goff in the yard. You'll have to scrub whole place down.'

'He were terrified you'd smack him one, George. That what did it,' laughs one of the women.

They take their time crossing the bridge and climbing Flowergate; the rain is falling thicker than ever and their cargo is too precious to drop. Even so Hutchinson's blubber-encrusted boots slide from under him twice, causing him to dent his nose on the flagstones. By the time the party reaches the mansion on Skinner Street, Robert and Tom are knackered.

Hutchinson removes all his clothes and stands naked in the rain while his men carry the keg indoors and re-emerge with soap and a brush.

'Don't stand there gawking, go and fetch the second keg.'

Wet hair plastered to their skulls like drowned rats, the lads head off down Skinner Street.

Finally, at half past one, smelling a shade less fetid and wrapped in a blanket, Harold calls his boys to join him in the snug before a roaring fire.

'So, what do we have?' Harold asks.

'Premium rum. Thirty gallons,' says Tom.

'Grand work, lads,' says Hutchinson. 'There's more than that hidden in the old town but given our circumstances not a bad night's work. Tomorrow we will pay the Old Ship Launch Inn a visit on Baxtergate and see what else is tucked away. So one barrel for His Majesty and the other goes in my cellar. In fact, fetch a pint up right now, Robert, I've built up a thirst. And while you're there, wake Mrs Seacombe and tell her to prepare me a second warming pan, that parky outdoor bath has left me chilled to the bone.'

By the time Harold Hutchinson enters his dining room the following morning and sits down to breakfast on a pair of Fortune's finest kippers, some 200 gallons of rum, 50 gallons of brandy, 3 casks of tobacco and 3 chests of tea, and 7 blunderbusses are hidden away in caves, hedges and hiding holes on the moors some six miles from Whitby, and five tired donkeys are heading back to Abbey Field.

Tom and Robert meanwhile sleep soundly on the cellar floor, each lad having received a large pouch of tobacco from smug George the Geordie, with the promise of more to come if they keep their bloody mouths shut.

Ballad of The Oak

Rebecca Anne Johnson had already done a full day's work by the time the sun was setting on that fateful day in 1803. Still only a young woman, her body ached from carrying, pressing, opening and turning. Her fair hair hung stiff with salt, her apron grubby with fish guts.

Young she was but old enough to remember the riot of 1793 when the town had turned on the press gangs and given them a good hiding.

It was the 23rd of February and some little time after seven in the evening when the crowd of almost a thousand townsfolk turned up outside the ale house on Haggersgate where the press gang were holding their rendezvous.

Since the 1750s Whitby had been a town with prospects as ship building and whaling had brought money and jobs. Forty years on, the whole population was skull-brimmed of the misery and mayhem brought by the gangs who would enter a town to steal able-bodied men and drag them off to serve on Royal Navy ships.

There were reasons the Navy struggled to find volunteers: the pay was rubbish, working conditions worse and up to half the men on any given ship might die of scurvy. Rates of desertion for volunteers and pressed men alike were sky high.

The Navy's own rules required the press gangs only take men between 18 and 55 years of age, and stipulated that whaling crews were exempted because of the value of their work, but the gangs did as they pleased and no one was safe. They swaggered into ale houses up and down the coast and kidnapped men at will on behalf of His Majesty's Navy.

And they particularly loved plundering Whitby.

Families would lose their husbands, fathers, sons. Entire households would be thrown into destitution so a king could conduct wars here there and everywhere.

Rebecca Anne Johnson had lost her grandfather and her father to the pressers and as a twelve-year-old she had accompanied her mother to the riot.

'I'll die sooner than let them take my boys,' her mother had said.

The women were among the ringleaders that day and had spent hours arming themselves for the night ahead. Hannah Hobson, whose husband had died at sea leaving her to raise three young bairns alone, led the women inland along the banks of the Esk to fill their sacks with rocks and stones.

The attack commenced in a frenzy of brickbats and stones that demolished every window in the ale house. For a while the press gang defended themselves, rightly fearing for their lives but the crowd was too large and too angry. At around nine o'clock the door of the ale house was finally smashed down and the mob swarmed in.

The press gang and the publican were beaten mercilessly and savagely thrown out onto the street, more dead than alive. Everything in the tavern was destroyed, smashed to pieces; furniture reduced to shards and fragments until all that remained were bare walls and gaping windows. Rebecca Anne had watched her mother and other adults she had known all her life turn into a raging sea of violence as they tried to rid their town of the press gangs once and for all.

The mob returned to Haggersgate the following night, Rebecca Anne's brothers, twelve and fourteen, still hidden safely away in a hedge near Hawsker. The idea was to dismantle the ale house brick by brick; to remove every last trace of it from the world.

They were too late. The army had arrived. The huge crowd dispersed but too slowly. Three ringleaders were seized and taken for trial in York. John Harrison was acquitted. Hannah Hobson and William Atkinson, however, were found guilty. Atkinson was hanged, while Hobson was deported to Australia on a convict ship.

The fishing community licked their wounds and mourned their dead. Atkinson, sail maker, had lost his two brothers to the gangs and Hannah Hobson had worked with Rebecca Anne's own mother, selling fish and taking in washing. Another brave woman who had stood up to protect kith and kin had paid the price, her three bairns now orphaned.

And so it was, at the back end of 1803, that Rebecca Anne Johnson, now twenty-two years of age and heavy with child, had rushed to join efforts to save the crew of The Oak from the menace of the press gangs as soon as news of the commotion reached the alleys off Church Street.

A ferocious storm had driven The Oak, a large whaling vessel, to seek refuge in the harbour. Captain Banks hadn't even dropped anchor before the gangs laid siege to the vessel in an attempt to press the entire crew into service for the Navy. Outraged Whitby folk poured out of their houses all around the harbour, screaming insults and banging pots and pans. It seemed a lost cause but the locals were not to be deflected, young and old alike gathered on the shore to make their voices heard and eventually in all the commotion and noise they managed to spirit the entire crew away to safety from under the noses of gangs through the maze of ghauts, ginnels, alleys and passages that led up between the houses.

The evening ended with the press gangs standing empty-handed on the beach while Rebecca Anne and hundreds more of her neighbours taunted and mocked them.

For a few weeks the crew of The Oak stayed up top, hiding on the moors and in the villages and countryside around Whitby, dressed as farm labourers, waiting for the press gang to give up and leave. And eventually they did leave and when they did the taverns opened their doors once more and jugs of ale passed from hand to hand.

Within days the ballad of The Oak was being

sung in every bar. You may still hear the song today, if the wind is blowing in the right direction.

Ballad of The Oak

'Twas caught in angry boiling seas they sought a solace sweet
In Whitby harbour where the best of whaler folk you meet
But as they sailed for sanctuary between the harbour jaws
The press gang came and seized the men before they reached the shore.

Though they were fit and better armed we crushed their evil plans
We took them on and drove them back just banging pots and pans
While they regrouped and charged again we held them back until
our lads had left the ginnels and run halfway up the hill

So strong The Oak that bears a crew
And strong the folk that turn the screw
To beat the pressers fair and square
And leave them clutching at thin air

We'll run them out of town
They'll never wear us down
We'll make all pressers croak
Before they'll take The Oak.

Pandora's Pavilion

She curses herself for dawdling in the ladies' toilets to adjust her makeup, but it's too late now. She is locked in the Pavilion and the phone lines are down round the entire building. She's checked.

No shortage of food, which is something. The cafeteria is awash with crisps, soft drinks and as many cups of tea and as she likes.

Security locks everywhere. She won't smash a window to get out. Just imagine the rumpus. Front page of the Gazette. She'd never live it down.

No, she will sit it out. The cleaners or the care-taker are bound to arrive soon. No need to worry; it's 1994 for goodness' sake, not the Dark Ages.

She wanders around, perusing the *What's On This*

Autumn posters in the reception area. She studies the menu in the cafeteria. Because there's no one there, she leans over the bar curious to see what lies under the counter then thinks, what the hell, and walks round to take a good look from the other side. Glasses, cups and saucers. A sink by the wall. Boxes of crisps and chocolate bars.

'What can I get you, Madam?' she pretends she is serving a customer. 'A coffee without cream? Certainly, Madam. Oh dear, I'm very sorry, we've run out of cream. Would you have it without *milk*?'

She wishes she had the courage to say such things in real life. That would shut them up.

She puts 30p on the counter and takes a packet of biscuits. The cellophane crackles between her fingertips as she enters the newly built Northern Lights hall, crosses to the huge windows and gazes at waves rolling onto West Cliff Beach below.

The music sneaks out of nowhere. A Hammond organ echoes in the empty space, as if the sound has travelled a million miles. Feeling the back of her hair move, she spins round. The room is full of old couples ballroom dancing in long flowing dresses or tuxedos, cheek to cheek, eyes half-closed. Round and round in a giant circle as if the room were a bath and they are slowly spinning towards the plughole.

She races back to the cafeteria, closing the door behind her. When she looks back the hall is empty.

It's calmer in the old building.

The corridor to the theatre-cum-cinema is lined with photos of old show business stars. The carpet hushes her sensible shoes.

It's not yet dark. Someone will pass by and raise the alarm. A lady walking her dog. A jogger.

She can't help herself. She's curious by nature. Maybe she missed a set of keys hanging behind one of the doors in the cinema. She pulls open a door and crosses the threshold.

The auditorium is muffled soft silent. In the subdued safety lighting all the chairs look towards the stage, waiting for the show to begin.

How many lovely shows and films has she seen here? Fifty? A hundred? She sits down to consider what she will do if night falls and no one comes.

She feels safe here in the old theatre.

A peel of laughter followed by enthusiastic applause. The stage is awash with light. It's a full house for *Marvo the Whitby Wonder*.

A spotlight swings round to bathe her in light.

'There she is!' cries Marvo. 'Ladies and Gentlemen, please join with me in welcoming her up onto the stage for the most bedazzling, bewonderful and bespectacular moment in showbusiness!'

She blushes, approaches and runs up the steps and onto the stage. Marvo has a member of the audience lying in a long box bearing the word *Pandora* in bright yellow along the side. The man's head and arms poke out one end, feet out the other.

'Grab one end,' Marvo says, offering her one of the handles of a giant saw, 'and, before your very eyes, we will saw this smashing gentleman in half!'

The gentleman is around fifty years of age. Spiked-up hair and large nose. Turquoise jacket.

The room holds its breath. The blade tugs back and forth. The gentleman screams convincingly and, when the blade is done, she pulls the sides of the box apart, curious to see inside. Blood puddles the floor.

The audience gasps.

Abruptly she is by herself on the empty stage, not bedazzled but bewildered, and somewhat lost. She curls up in a foetal position and wishes she might sleep.

When she awakes she is thirsty. She leaves the empty theatre and heads to the cafeteria. Dawn sunshine shimmers the shifting sea.

Someone behind the bar is doing the washing up, which pleases her no end. The nightmare is over.

'Can I have a cup of tea?' she asks.

'Of course, Madam. Lovely morning for it.' He looks over his shoulder and smiles.

'Yes, it is,' she agrees.

The water is coming to a boil. He drops a tea bag in the cup and reaches for the jug of milk.

'Saucer,' he says, scratching his spiky hair.

Something about the way he moves down the bar puzzles her. She lifts herself up on her toes to peer over the bar and gasps.

The man doesn't exist from the waist down. Nothing there at all. A bead of blood drips from the bottom of his turquoise jacket. He turns. 'Your tea, Madam,' he smiles.

Before she can pick it up, her arms have gone, as have her eyes, face, torso. She staggers blindly, bumps into the counter and crumples to the floor.

Eight o'clock.

'Are you all right, Mavis?'

'Not really.'

Mavis is in her uniform behind the counter.

'I tidied up last night,' Eric Dunn, the caretaker assures her. 'Everything should be in order.'

'Same as last time,' Mavis says. '30p on the counter, an untouched cup of tea, and drops of blood on the linoleum.'

Consummate Cook

If you visit the Whale Bone Arch on West Cliff, take a moment to look at the statue of Captain Cook and observe what he is holding in his right hand.

It is all but forgotten nowadays that Captain Cook introduced the nation to a whole new culinary world of experience.

Born in the village of Marton near Middlesbrough then apprenticed to a draper in Staithes, a small fishing community eleven miles north of Whitby, James Cook always loved his food. As a child he loved nothing more than making chocolate muffins with his mother. Later, when he wasn't discovering New Zealand or charting the eastern coast of Australia, he was forever dropping anchor by pacific islands, popping into their exotic markets, trading with the locals and buying new ingredients to test on his crew.

In 1769, on his first expedition to the Pacific, Cook wrote that "while enjoying a singing Festival with the local population on the uninhabited island of Karaoke we were taken to the Downtown area and did visit Sushi bars and Cantonese restaurants where perchance we found ourselves offered divers sweet-meats, fruits, food parcels, and other Comestibles served in small bowls.

"It is apparently the Custom to eat the foods with the aid of two Twigs held between the Fingers. The Japanese call these sticks hashi or otemoto, while the Chinese call them kuàizi. After some little time we mastered the Skill and found it much to our Liking; and the local population confessed they much preferred to watch us eating rather than suffer the injury of our Singing."

Some weeks later on the archipelago of Manga and Anime, Cook and his party were again served a similar feast by local dignitaries. On this occasion however no utensils were presented. Upon learning that they were all to eat with their fingers, Captain Cook delicately explained to his hosts how food was consumed on the uninhabited island of Karaoke and enquired as to whether it might be possible to emulate that approach by sending someone into the rainforest to *chop sticks* that they might use.

The rest is, of course, history.

With commendable understatement the plaque beneath Cook's statue does not even mention the pair of chopsticks in his right hand nor the sushi rolling mat tucked under his left arm; focusing exclusively and modestly on his seafaring exploits.

It is often remarked that a great cook is known as much for the dishes they prepare as for the distance they travel to work and the same is unquestionably true of James Cook. He was forever in the ship's galley preparing new treats for his men. In his journal he describes a favourite pudding as being made from 'Breadfruit, ripe Bananas, Taro and Pandanus Nuts mixed with Coca nutt Cream and cooked with hot stones from the oven'.

Elsewhere he describes 'deliciously cool cocoa nutts', though his entry is unclear as to this was in the context of food or earrings. According to the ship's Gunner, Stephen Forwood, Cook's breadfruit scones were 'to die for', while others credited his sweet potato, ahee and wharra lasagne with ensuring that the crew escaped scurvy.

All that said, Cook was not uncritical of local culinary traditions, writing of Tahitian cuisine that 'cookery seems to have been but little studied here; they only have 2 Methods of applying Fire-broiling and Baking, as we call it. The Method this is done I have before described, and I am of the Opinion that Victuals dressed this way are more juicy and more equally done that by any of our Methods, large Fish in particular, Bread Fruit, Bananoes, Plaintains Cooked this way eat like boil'd Potatoes, and was much used by us by way of bread whenever we could get them.'

High praise from a man used to employing a blowtorch to put the finishing touches on his crème brulé, and a Belgian waffle iron to prepare his Captain's Special crèpes suzettes.

Indeed upon the Endeavour's return to Whitby, Cook had a troublesome time persuading his crew to leave the ship, so used were they to the exceptionally high standards of cuisine on board.

'It's either stay on board and eat like gentlemen or step ashore and go back to slops and gruel,' said able-bodied seaman William Peckover.

'Aye, it's not as if they have even invented chips yet,' added downcast Quartermaster, James Gray.

Reckless Lovers

It is a little-known fact that in November 2016 Whitby was invaded by the Scravir.

Whitby Goth Weekend that year saw the surprise appearance of Goth superstar, Thor Lupei, and his band Hounds of Hellbane. While the fans were in raptures at the music at the Pavilion a major storm was brewing.

The heavens opened as the Hounds of Hellbane took to the stage. The night was thick with rain. Around the lighthouse a sea of gulls raced inland to seek sanctuary among the chimney pots in the old town. The Henrietta, a small fishing trawler, was caught between the harbour jaws. In a matter of minutes the boat was smashed to slithers, its crew airlifted to safety as the boiling sea ripped the hull into a thousand fragments.

Earlier that day the police had been called to sites in the old town where three emaciated corpses had been found, and the town's pathologist, Dr Nigela Shaveling, worked into the night conducting autopsies to ascertain what had happened.

While most people did what most people do in these circumstances - stay indoors under cover - some exotic souls saw a huge storm on the sea as a source of unbridled excitement. So it was for Jason Warren and Violet Cooke. In Whitby for the first time, having travelled from Manchester to give their top hats an airing, the lovers decided huge waves smacking the harbour walls would be the perfect backdrop for a snog and maybe something more.

Leaving their bed & breakfast, her in a purple bodice beneath her steam punk tuxedo coat, him in a hired Victorian undertaker vibe complete with gloves and long grey wig, they made their way across the swing bridge towards Church Street.

The winds were gale force. Many would have been discouraged at almost losing their top hat and seeing their wig fly off over the upper harbour. The lovers were, after all, still hundreds of metres from the sea and comparatively sheltered, but our two love birds saw this unfortunate incident as proof positive that the best place to be on such a lacklit night would be on a stone bench of the East Pier facing the full fury of wind and waves. And so they hurried along Sandgate, Church Street, and Henrietta Street until finally they stood by the last of the cottages, over-looking the harbour jaws, their neck muscles strain-ing to keep their heads on their shoulders, their faces pricked by the icy rain, and their coat tails flapping noisily behind them like farting angels.

The further they went, the more exposed they became. The cobbles seemed to slide about under-foot. The lampposts rattled and shook. The gale whistled and roared and still our lovers pressed on, now starting their descent down the steep path to-wards the pier.

Like tumbleweed in a two-horse wild west town, a large black waste bin rolled and bounced as it passed the couple, heading inland onto Henrietta Street. The silhouette of the cliff above them was all but invisible, so dark had the night become.

'What do you think?' Jason asked tremulously, in a rare moment of self-awareness.

'It's brilliant. Like that scene in Death of a Vampire,' Violet replied, pulling strands of wet hair out of her mouth. 'Let's do it!'

'Yeah, let's do it!' Jason echoed.

Bravado is sometimes contagious.

The path below was even more treacherous than the cobbles above. They clung to each other like limpets while the roar of the wind escalated. Earlier in the day they had perused the information board on the headland and had learned that for years there had been a bridge connecting the hill to the pier. Now there was only the path and a wooden handrail.

And then the handrail was gone.

And they still had not reached the lowest point. If they had sought a reason to stop and go back they had one now because, where they stood, the waves were exploding against the rocks in three metre high walls of water that drenched the lovers from head to toe. Salt in their mouths, they could barely read the red warning signs as they inched gingerly over the fossils prints that had been stamped in the concrete. The water sloshed back and forth up one ramp and down the other. Into the harbour, out to the sea. When seconds later Violet lost her footing, dragging Jason down with her, it looked like the water might drag them both away into the fatal bowels of the deep.

They could no longer even hear each other shout above the chaos of noise that engulfed them. They laughed as only those determined to win a Darwin Award can laugh, picked themselves up and continued up the last short stretch of path onto the harbour wall of the east pier.

The east pier is a rugged brute, more than twenty metres wide in places and fashioned from giant slabs of rock. It was built to face fearlessly the full force of the sea. It is also for the most part quite flat and, wet and wind-swept as it was on this particular night, somewhat exposed to the elements.

Undeterred, our two halfwits (for it is time to be honest and call them what they were) continued heading towards what they believed would be the ultimate location for a bit of Gothic smooching.

Forget the mile high club, forget a grass hut on stilts over a coral reef in the South Pacific, forget the Eifel Tower at dusk, forget standing in a Land Rover on the Serengeti as a million wildebeest sweep past majestically on their annual migration, forget reclining with your beloved in a gondola on a Venetian canal while your gondolier croons Nessun Dorma. You can even forget sitting down to two happy meals at Leicester Forest Services on the M1.

Forget all of that. For Jason and Violet, nirvana was Whitby's East Pier in a gale; wedged between stone and pouring sky as a bitter North Sea hurled all the world's water at Whitby.

On their hands and knees they traversed the last twenty metres like mountaineers climbing the North Wall of the Eiger.

Reaching their goal, they sat a moment on the frozen stones, a brutal concrete wall at their backs, revelling in their triumph. They had nailed a perfect moment. A forever moment that would stay with them until they drew their last breaths.

In spite of the intense cold, the flames of passion drew them close and, wrapped in each other's arms they kissed.

One of the problems with forever moments, especially if you choose to close your eyes to kiss, is that all too quickly the backdrop disappears entirely and you might as well be sprawled across the sofa in your bedsit or on the back seat of the bus on your way to work. The world vanishes as fingers fumble and saliva mingles.

And so it was for Violet and Jason. Worse still, they had already spent most of the day fondling and smooching. Their lips were chaffed with kissing. They had missed the news about the strange deaths in the town. They certainly had never heard the word *Scravir*. Had they been paying more attention they might have felt less invincible in Whitby during a storm on the weekend when the Hounds of Hellbane were in town.

Lost in their little bubble of love, cocooned in the rushing rain and howling walls, the pounding winds and screaming wave wraiths, they were paying no attention to anything other than each other's caresses and puckering lips.

It didn't occur to either of them to question how many lover's hands were touching them or how it was that the beloved other could be fondling both their chest and their lower back ... and their neck.

Nor did they pay attention to the slip-sliding sensation of flesh vanishing from their abdomens; their hearts were too hot and their bodies were too numb with cold to notice such little things. And because their eyes were closed they did not see the tall gentleman with the long white hair leaning over the stone wall, fingers outstretched and lightly pressing the napes of their necks.

Thor Lupei, for it was he, was also loving the moment. There was something perfect about being the incognito third lover. Adept at getting beneath the skin of his victims, Lupei absorbed their passions vicariously through his fingertips even as he was removing their viscera, drawing into himself slippery brown kidneys that wriggled like trout in a stream, siphoning sweetbreads, consuming corneas, and inhaling ovaries with effortless ease.

How sweet and trusting lovers were. How utterly self-absorbed, to the point of folly. Life was but a fleet fickle fading flower. Hey, ding a ding ding.

Eyes open, Lupei breathed deep, relishing the roaring elements. A glorious moment in a perfect evening.

By the time the lovers started to feel the theft of their vitals, it was too late. Lupei, not wanting pain or anguish to spoil his evening, quickly extinguished their hearts and two lives evaporated into the thunderous slip-sleek lacklight. The stones that had sheltered the lovers from voyeuristic eyes now hid them from help. No one had seen a thing.

Lupei jumped down from the wall and casually rolled the two bodies over the edge into the boiling sea. He strolled away, a little more slowly than he had arrived as he was carrying extra weight.

Several days later a couple who had gone to Ravenscar noticed two bodies in one of the shallow rock pools beneath the cliff, first mistaking them for seals. By then identification was impossible.

So if you feel tempted to smooch on the East Pier in a dark and violent storm, keep an eye out for extra hands. It is such a shame to spoil a perfect moment.

Grand Day Out

'Good Lord, Phoebe, what on earth is the matter?' says Tobias Lightfoot.

Phoebe Lightfoot is distraught and quite unable to speak. Instead, she clutches her handkerchief to her bosom and sniffs.

'I am at a loss for words, I really am,' continues her husband, who clearly isn't. 'I have made every effort to make you happy, have I not? On this day of all days. In front of the whole town.'

Phoebe glances briefly up at her husband then glances to her right and is once again overwhelmed by sobs.

Just five minutes ago, Phoebe was all smiles, excited, animated, and exchanging pleasantries with

Mr and Mrs Pickersgill, interrupting them while they whispered sweet-nothings in each other's ears. She beamed happily at the Bradshawes, even though she finds Mrs Bradshawe a dreadful snob. She even found the courage to introduce herself to the short gentleman in white breeches, navy frock coat, a silk scarf cravat and a gibus collapsible top hat standing behind her in the queue. Fergus O'Connor is on a mission. He left Newcastle yesterday evening destined for Dublin and, should he get there in record time, will trouser twenty-three golden guineas.

Right along the length of the queue everyone was abuzz with anticipation of the adventure ahead. Townsfolk gathered across the street, gawping.

And then the long curtain that was to be officially opened as part of the ceremony rippled in the breeze and Phoebe saw beyond it and her excitement deflated like a punctured balloon.

Phoebe's family are from Newcastle. For the past eight years, ever since she married Toby and moved with him to Whitby, she has endured her brother Molesworth's awful and almost monthly letters in which he gloats incessantly that Newcastle is the epicentre of the world and Whitby but a sleepy backwater. That letter where he boasted that Stephenson's Rocket, built in Newcastle's Forth

Street Works if you please, was to be entered in the Rainhill Trials of October 1829 organised by Liverpool and Manchester Railways. That horrid little card from her mother, her own mother, crowing in the most indecent terms that the Rocket had won the competition.

Phoebe has been so looking forward to today; the perfect opportunity to turn the tables and prove to her wretched family that Whitby, and not Newcastle, is the very hub of modernity.

'What is the matter with your wife?' enquires Mr Bradshawe, leaning round Mrs Bradshawe's ample frame to identify the source of the sobbing.

'I have no idea, Sir,' Tobias insists. 'Please accept my apologies.'

'Must be nerves at the thought of the speed at which we will be travelling,' Mr Bradshawe suggests. 'Ten miles an hour! Womenfolk are fragile gentle souls.'

Mrs Bradshawe pulls her husband abruptly back into line.

'Can I implore you to think of others?' Tobias tells Phoebe in a low but aggressive hiss. 'This is an auspicious day for the entire town. Whitby has waited so long for this. Mr Bradshawe and the bank will take a very dim view of the scene you are making. It might even disadvantage my prospects.'

'Ladies and Gentlemen,' says a voice to their right.

All heads turn. The mayor is standing on a raised platform in his best suit, his top hat gleaming in the morning sunshine.

'I am proud, nay, inordinately honoured to welcome you on this most historic occasion. People will look back with pride and say that 1836 marked the dawn of a new era for our town. A day of glory and unparalleled achievement as Whitby joins the age of the railway!

'*Railway?*' Phoebe mutters sarcastically under her breath.

'Yes, railway,' Tobias hisses. 'And if you cannot have regard of the impression you are making on others then at least have the courtesy to think about *me* for a moment.'

The mayor is still talking. 'And so, without further ado, it gives me immense, nay, immeasurable pleasure to invite you all to come forward and step aboard the first Whitby to Pickering railway service!'

He grabs the ceremonial cord and pulls it sharply downwards and the crimson curtains part.

'I officially declare this new and most auspicious adventure open for business!'

The air fills with applause and cries of hurrah, hurrah! Church bells peal. Hats are tossed into the air and the queue of dignitaries files forwards towards the train.

Phoebe shuffles forwards past the curtain then stops.

'For heaven's sake, Phoebe!' Tobias expostulates 'What now?'

But Phoebe has had enough of the whole charade. She holds her ground and turns towards her husband, arms akimbo, her voice thick with emotion. 'Where is Stephenson's glorious Rocket?'

'What?'

'Where is his rocket? The train. Where is the train? This isn't a railway. You promised me.'

'For goodness' sake, Phoebe, the railway is right in front of you. I must protest. This really is most obtuse.'

'That is not a train, Toby. In case you haven't noticed, it does not go puff puff, there is no chimney, no bright yellow paint, no pistons, nothing. Your *train* has four ears and one half of it has just pooped on the track.'

'Oh, is that all?' Tobias says, relieved to have at last got to the bottom of his wife's anguish. 'This is a horse-drawn railway, my love.'

'If I want to be pulled about by horses I can climb into a stagecoach, Toby, as people have done for hundreds of years. This isn't a special occasion, it's a travesty.'

'Please keep your voice down,' Tobias hisses.

'And look at the carriages. They're just the bodies of dismantled stagecoaches glued together and stuck up on funny wheels.'

'Are you coming aboard?' asks the newly appointed stationmaster in his equally new uniform, as he steps between the arguing couple and smiles encouragingly. 'We are due to leave in a couple of minutes.'

Tobias Lightfoot nods his thanks. Mr Bradshawe, staring pointedly at his fob watch, is seated beside his wife. Opposite them Mr and Mrs Pickersgill whisper happy nothings. Mr O'Connor stares towards the horizon and pictures his twenty-three guineas. Tobias stares pathetically at his wife.

Phoebe sighs, looks to the heavens and rolls her eyes.

'Oh, all right. But I'm warning you, Toby, I have a bellyful of disappointment. If afternoon tea at the Black Swan in Pickering turns outs to be nothing more than pot of gruel or an apple I shall scream.'

Look Lively

Gentle waves fold and furl beneath the bows of the boat as she heads out in a straight line like a needle stitching the seam on a pair of blue jeans.

'Will we see them, Dad?' Charley asks.

'Who knows, Kiddo. It's like Captain Cook up there on the hill; one day you're the statue, the next you're the seagull. We just have to be lucky.'

Charley and Daniel run from one side to the other, laughing like pirates and peering down into the depths, hoping to glimpse something moving beneath the broken reflections of the clouds.

The skipper is not looking down, his gaze is fixed on the horizon. As Whitby's harbour jaws shrink to nothing behind the boat, Captain Oyston is in his element. He hears the tourists and he hears something else too; the creaking of rigging and the sound of ice pressing against the hull.

After 30 minutes he spots the gannets and, moments, later a dark back arches briefly and submerges.

'Ahoy, ahead to starboard!' Oyston calls out. 'A minke whale. There she blows!'

The tourists and nature lovers turn excitedly as the boat approaches the frenzy of gannets. There are hundreds of them diving and popping up on the surface. The sea is bursting, boiling with life and punctuating the waves between the birds are seals and whales.

Oyston has discharged his duty. He observes his happy crew laughing and taking photographs and smiles, and remembers another crew long long ago.

'Aren't they amazing?' cries the woman in the blue anorak. 'It must be more than ten metres long!'

Aye, ten metres and more, thinks Oyston, and a thing of rare beauty but dwarfed all the same by the leviathans of Greenland's artic waters.

A long shadow drifts beneath the boat.

Oyston never tires of the sound of the sea, it is woven through the fabric of his soul. The shlick, shlick of ripples kissing the bows, the hollow splashes of the diving gannets, the wind that whistles the rigging, and the explosive eruption of a breeching whale.

The girl Charley must be all of eight years old and her younger brother maybe six. Oyston remembers his own children at the same age, brimful of beans, without a care. He feels a familiar pang of guilt and regret that he left them for months at a time. All those laze-about hazy days warm with summer rain and August sunshine that he missed because he was two and a half thousand miles away battling bloody and raw, crushed between grey skies and a frozen sea.

'Do you see whales every day?' asks Daniel, suddenly at Oyston's side, his eyes wide as Wednesdays.

'Every day,' Oyston confirms. 'Even on my days off. Even in my sleep.'

The boy gives him a curious look and runs off to his sister.

It is the best day for a week. After the two minkes comes a pod of bottlenose dolphins, weaving, rolling, clicking, creaking. Everyone on board is thick with emotion as the sun arcs slowly above them. Oyston brings the boat round gently to prolong the moment of contact and allow his motley crew of landlubbers to breathe deep the symphony of the sea.

But his mind is elsewhere. As the boat rocks languidly back and forth Oyston is transported to another place, back to the night that never releases him.

The *Lively* left early on the 7th of March. Its master, Captain Kirk, took only mechanics and officers as he left Whitby. The ship's owners, focused as ever on money, had decided to hire a crew in Shetland where wages were lower. They left at the sharp end of March in order to reach Greenland in time for the seal hunt, but the best time for seal hunting was also the most dangerous time to be at sea, enduring endless driving gales and long nights surrounded by shifting skirts of ice.

Captain Oyston had also set sail for the Greenland Sea at that time, on the *Mary*. The further they travelled the worse the weather became, deteriorating with every passing hour. Up in the rigging, the crew of the *Mary* lashed themselves to the masts and Oyston tied himself to the wheel to avoid being swept overboard by the mountainous waves. Great slabs of ice smacked against the hull, damaging her greatly. Below deck the crew fell silent, fearing that the many hazards assailing them might sink the ship.

As dusk fell, crewman Lack, high in the rigging, shouted and pointed. Some little distance away was another ship and Captain Oyston, though unable to see clearly, decided it must be the *Lively*. After a few minutes he lost sight of her in the terrible swell.

A hand is tugging at his sleeve. Oyston pulled from his memories looks down to see the girl, Charley, at his side. The sounds of summer rush back. The fish must have left the surface for deeper water because the gannets are now high diving and hitting the surface at up to seventy miles per hour to take them down among the shoals.

'Are you all right?' she asks, her brow furrowed with worry.

'Yes, child,' he says.

'Can you tell us if they're porpoises or dolphins? My dad says porpoises, but porpoises are quite small, aren't they?'

Oyston allows himself to be led by the hand towards the front of the boat. Three bottlenose dolphins are playing under the bow, rushing this way then that, clouds of bubbles rising in their wakes.

'Dolphins,' he tells her.

'Yay!' shouts the girl, letting go of his hand to do a little jig of celebration, with her tongue out, in front of her father.

Oyston is turning to head back down the ship when he stops in his tracks. One of the passengers has dropped their sandwiches in the sea and squares of soggy bread are floating and turning softly slowly on the surface and Oyston is sucked back through the vortex of lost time to a different colder sea.

It is the 2nd of September 1826. Dawn has finally broken and the gales have abated. The seas have cleared of ice and two casks on which are stencilled the word *Lively* are bobbing in the swell surrounded by hundreds of ship's biscuits.

She went down with all hands.

Oyston feels his head spinning.

He wakes up, lying on the deck, anxious passengers gathered around him.

'See? I told you he wasn't dead,' Daniel tells Charley. 'He just fell asleep, that's all, because he's old. That's what old people do.'

Oyston is helped to his feet. He mutters his thanks and returns aft. The sun shines all the way back to Whitby. The passengers, having decided that the Captain is fine and all is well, are now chatting animatedly about their adventure and looking at each other's phones and laughing at the photos they have taken. In a few hours they have all become friends.

The boat passes through the harbour jaws and past the lighthouse and enters the calm waters of the harbour.

A few minutes later the boat is berthed at Brewery Steps and Oyston is helping people to step ashore.

'That was the best day of my life,' Daniel announces solemnly, while saluting the captain.

'There really are whales! It's amazing!' Charley calls out to a couple leaning over the railing on St Ann's Staith.

'Aye,' Oyston says quietly to himself. 'Lucky we didn't kill them all.'

They have almost reached the swing bridge when Charley realises she didn't thank the captain. She turns and runs back towards Brewery Steps but when she gets there the boat has gone. In its place she sort of sees a large wooden ship with three tall masts, half there half not there, and on the deck is a man who looks like Captain Oyston in olden day clothes talking to a group of sailors.

She rubs her eyes and the ship is gone.

All that remains are a few dozen biscuits floating in the harbour around a couple of partially submerged casks bearing the word *Lively*.

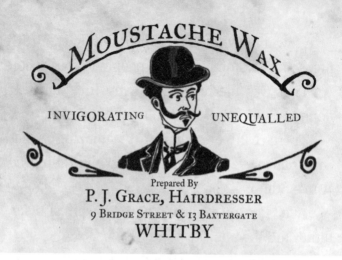

Festival Weekend

John Flintoff wakes up as they are leaving Ruswarp. He loves the smell of the train, the tickety-tack, the clouds of steam and soot, the hollow hoot of the whistle.

With only five minutes before the train arrives, John stands to collect his luggage from the rack, a medium-sized brown leather suitcase and his hatbox.

The brakes squeal and the train comes to a stop. Whitby. The platform is awash with people, many dressed normally, some of them dressed anything but normally. John threads his way towards the exit, trying not to gawp too obviously.

Out on the street it is harder to avoid looking at people. Festival weekend is a magnet for the bizarre.

He never tires of seeing all the work that people have put into the contraptions and contrivances they carry with them and loves the invention and creativity.

This year, as last year, the fashion is for little black boxes, like cigars cases possibly made of jet or such-like, that are carried in the hand and often close to the face. Grown men and women walk with hesitant steps while they make a show of peering into the boxes, as if reading, or hold forth very animatedly as they promenade, as if in conversation with spirits. Very entertaining and quite peculiar! So focused are the participants on their performance that sometimes they risk injury to their persons by stepping into the road without looking to see their path is clear.

Then there are the costumes; a cornucopia of imaginative ingenuity. Strange hats, gowns, and eyewear, all calculated to astonish in equal measure. Men and women sporting shiny jackets or frock coats in the most extraordinary hues and shapes; some bearing writing in the manner of a sandwich board.

As usual there are individuals wandering the streets without any form of headwear at all though, thankfully, the majority of people are very respectably dressed.

John steps aside to avoid a couple approaching in the opposite direction wearing spectacles of such strange shape and colour as to resemble the iridescent eyes of a fly. The lady is staring intently into one of the flat face boxes and the gentleman is guiding her. While he has no idea how the spectacles achieve their polychromasia, John is confident that such devices may be purchased at Lattimore's Gentleman's Shop on Bridge Street.

Having enjoyed a walk, John heads for his lodgings on Loggerheads Yard. A creature of habit, he always stays at the same place. The owner, a Mary Havelock, spirit merchant and grocer on Baxtergate, hasn't been around to greet him on his most recent visits but, since he always pays in advance by cheque, she long ago gave him a key to let himself in and out.

Though he has said nothing to Mrs Havelock, John is increasingly dismayed at the condition of the property. For so many years a temple of cleanliness, there are now weeds on the doorstep, dust in the hall, and the disagreeable odour of mildew on the stairs. The steps creak as he climbs to his attic room.

John is a whiskerando and sports a splendid set of Dundreary whiskers. Before he does anything else he wipes the dust from the dressing table then sets out his grooming kit: the finest French AK razor, strop, shaving brush and soap, moustache wax and comb, snood and finally his favourite violet flower pomade, made to order from fresh violets, beef suet and lard. Attention turns to the rest of his belongings: spare shirt, a couple of collars, second waistcoat, and his cravats. When all is arranged to his satisfaction, he checks his fob watch then reads a book until darkness falls. He has his nap then, refreshed, ventures out into the evening.

It is very mild for the time of year and John feels the urge to unbutton his jacket and waistcoat. But he is a gentleman and leaves his attire as it is. He crosses the bridge and turns left onto Church Street where he enters the back room of the White Horse and Griffin. They have a room set aside for travellers like himself and he is soon tucking into crab omelette, whiting pudding, a flagon of ale and a coffee.

At the end of Henrietta Street are the 199 steps towards the Abbey. The smell of rain hangs in the air. On reaching the church at the top of the steps, John circumnavigates the graveyard, breathing in the sea air and pausing to pay his respects in front of the grave.

There follows an awkward moment when he finds himself face to face with two females with purple hair, who appear to have forgotten half their clothes and are displaying an extravagant amount of flesh. No matter how many festivals he attends, John will never acclimatise to such eccentricity.

He feels similarly uncomfortable at the troubling decline in hat etiquette; so many gentlemen abuse the auspices of a festival to abandon hat raising altogether.

John avoids the Pavilion, having once made the error of following the crowds up the Khyber Pass steps whereupon he discovered that the building played host to an industrial exhibition in the evenings involving the most infernal cacophony of mechanical noises, so disquieting as to leave him fearing for his senses.

Back at his lodgings he dons his moustache snood and prepares for bed.

John wakes to the cries of the gulls. He rubs his eyes, removes his snood, applies lather to his chin and shaves until it is as smooth as a freshly-laid egg. He waxes and trims his moustache, combs his whiskers, works pomade through his hair and parts it down the middle, gets dressed and, donning his hat, steps out into Loggerheads Yard.

The sky is blue. At the back bar of the White Horse and Griffin he breakfasts on kippers and is ready to enjoy the day.

Yesterday he managed to ignore the preternatural modes of festival transportation that fill the street with noise and malodorous exhausts. This morning it is all but impossible. Personal carriages wait in a long line to cross the bridge. Most curious to John is that, for all its inventiveness, the Whitby festival imagines a future where transportation is neither electric nor steam-powered but designed around engines that belch foul and mephitic vapours. While the metal carriages are ingenious, even visionary, in form and colour, they appear designed to poison the air. John Flintoff is unsure he could ever live permanently in such a dystopia.

Having attended the Sunday service at St Mary's Church, sitting in his normal box pew, John returns to the old town. He spends until luncheon promenading on the periphery of the crowds, observing the performers and exhibitionists in their fancy clothes. He nods from time to time in acknowledgement of sartorial distinction but sees very few whiskers worth remembering. While it is satisfying to be the best coiffed gentleman in Whitby, John fears for a future where men lose the grooming skills that have shaped civilisation and defined the empire.

After a luncheon of cold meats and pickles, John

strolls along the east pier and watches the ever-changing sea. Shortly after four o'clock he ventures up to St Mary's one last time to offer his respects at the gravestone then makes his way to the station.

'All aboard the nineteen hundred service to Ruswarp and Grosmont. The train leaves in one minute.'

The last carriage door slams shut, the station master blows his whistle and John puts his cases up on the rack. He sits down and stretches his legs in front of him. The hypnotic rhythm of the pistons slowly building speed soothes him and the cares of the day fall away. Reflections of lights across the valley shimmer and dance on the river.

John's eyes drift shut. It's been a good festival weekend.

A little way upstream, two lads lean against their bikes looking towards the railway tracks, Ruswarp station at their backs. Purple black clouds kiss the treetops. It's so misty they can barely see the other side of the river.

'It won't happen. Yer talking keck,' says Luke. 'Bloody waste of time.'

'Shut up and watch,' Ryan replies. 'Look, there's the steam! It's coming.'

A plume of white steam billows over the trees, bright against the clouds.

They hear the train before they see it, then suddenly it's there, rushing towards them, hugging the riverbank. The black locomotive is pulling four carriages that may or may not be dark brown; it's hard to see in the failing light.

Ryan starts counting down 'seven, six, five, wait for it, two ...'

Just before he reaches one it happens.

The train starts to lose substance.

'WHAT? No way!'

'I *told* you!'

The train is still moving but it is haemorrhaging atoms like a sandcastle in a gale on Whitby sands. And it isn't slowing down.

Luke glances towards Ruswarp station. They haven't closed the barriers! He flings his bike round, clambers onto the saddle and races off.

Ryan makes no effort to follow him. He watches the train fly past, the river now clearly visible through the carriages. The train that contains the sleeping John Flintoff will disappear into the ether long before it reaches the station.

It always does.

The Whale Bone Archers

The last Whalebone Archer tournament in Whitby takes place in 1933.

It has been a busy year. The English cricket team won the Ashes, someone imagined they saw the Loch Ness Monster, and Bing Crosby has had a new hit record out every thirty-seven minutes.

The archer tournament rules are strict; the participants must use bows made from whalebone.

This is beginning to be a problem because the Whitby whaling industry ended in 1837 and the men who sailed the Greenland Sea are long dead. Fashioning bows from whalebone is a skill the whaling crews learned from the Eskimos who were excellent bow makers. Scrimshaw work - carving whale teeth, baleen, and walrus tusks into gifts for loved ones - was a way of staying sane on long voyages where months could pass with nothing happening.

Jeremiah Coulson, last of the Whitby whalebone carvers, has recently died. While too young to have sailed on a whaler, Jeremiah learned scrimshawing from his grandfather and his father. Who will carve whalebone bows now?

The entrants gather pre-dawn by Captain Cook's Monument on West Cliff. There is a stiff breeze off the sea that will play havoc with the arrows. A brief fracas occurs when one of the competitors, George Ferndill, sneaks away from the group, produces a handheld Bakelite anemometer to measure the wind speed and then refuses to divulge what he has learned to the others. The device ends up in pieces on Khyber Pass at the foot of the cliff and an assortment of thick ears and a broken nose are throbbing before the judge and his team have even finished their breakfasts at the Royal Hotel.

The anemometer is not the only concern. The tournament is open to all-comers and this year one of the nine is ... a woman! There have been several off-colour remarks, some ill-natured muttering about what the world may or may not be coming to, and some appalling jokes that were already old at Agincourt.

'What's she doing here?' whines Harry Holbroke from Sheffield.

'Must have pulled a few strings, Harry,' smirks Thomas Potts, a regular entrant.

Margaret Featherstone, great granddaughter of Adeline Featherstone, one-time gardener on Spring Gardens, keeps herself to herself. She has been practising hard for months ever since discovering the beautiful and exquisitely carved bow in a chest in the attic, along with the note crewman Hugh Dridon gave Adeline upon his return from his last whaling voyage a hundred years ago.

The markers have arrived below and are setting out the target to the left of the bandstand by the harbour, not that the archers are any the wiser because the bandstand isn't visible from the statue. Or from the Whalebone Arch.

At five past six the judge and his team emerge from the Royal Hotel and cross East Terrace towards the competitors. Two of the men are shouldering a dozen quivers.

'Now then,' says Charles Dunn, who has been head judge for twenty-seven years. He wears his chain of office and the Whalebone Archer Society's ceremonial tricorne sealskin hat, made in 1818 by Seaman Robert Gambel.

'Now then,' reply all the competitors except George Ferndill whose ears are ringing from the fracas and is hearing very little.

'I trust everyone has read the rules. We'll start with bow inspection while Gordon here runs down to check arrangements down by bandstand. You'll receive four dozen arrows each and last arrow must be shot by five to seven. Anyone shooting after whistle is blown will be disqualified and likely arrested. Understood?'

Nods of agreement as Gordon, a large fellow not obviously built for running up and down steps, lumbers off.

Assistant Francis Bovel, a skinny man who serves behind the linen counter at Woolworths, checks everyone has brought an authentic whalebone bow. He turns to Dunn.

'Everything is in order,' he whispers.

'Speak up, Bovel,' barks Dunn.

'Everything is in order,' he repeats, his voice shaking. He hates confrontation of any kind.

'Right, gentlemen … and lady. Follow me.'

Dunn leads them to the Whalebone Arch, where he produces a stick of chalk to mark the Narwhal

Line, so called because the first time the competition was held in 1863 a narwhal tusk was laid out to mark the shooting line behind which the archers must stand.

'No barging, no pushing. You'll fire sets of six then step back to allow the next man, or woman, to fire their arrows. Understood?' Dunn turns back to Bovel. 'Quivers.'

Bovel hands shake as he offers each competitor a quiver containing forty-eight arrows with shafts of a particular colour while Bovel's assistant, a spotty lad just starting his apprenticeship in the boatyards, scribbles down each entrant's name alongside the colour of arrows assigned to them.

They wait a good five minutes before Gordon, very red in the face, appears at the top of Khyber Pass steps. He staggers the last yards up to the Whalebone Arch.

'By the powers invested in me, I declare the course be set,' Gordon wheezes and collapses on the grass.

Charles Dunn ignores Gordon's attention-seeking antics. He turns to the competitors and counts off the seconds on his fob watch.

'May the winds be in your favour. May your arrows be harpoons and may the best man … or lady

… WIN!'

Dunn steps aside and the chaos begins.

Between them the nine archers must stand under the Whalebone Arch and discharge four hundred and thirty-two arrows in half an hour. That is one shot every four seconds or so. The target is one hundred and thirty yards from the arch and over the brow of the cliff. The archers cannot see the target from the Whalebone Arch. Those who have done their home-work know that the bandstand is a couple of degrees to the right of the lamppost that stands on the edge of the path ahead of them.

The only person who knows the strength of the wind is George Ferndill who hasn't heard a single instruction Dunn uttered.

In the seventy years of competition the target has only been struck six times. Three times more seagulls have been struck by stray arrows than have hit the target. Five car tyres have been punctured. In 1908 the captain of the *Fortunate*, a small fishing boat, had his hat shot from his head in the harbour. And a gentleman who fell asleep while availing himself of the public conveniences on Khyber Pass had to be taken to hospital suffering from shock after an arrow smashed through the frosted glass and embedded itself in the door of his cubicle. That no one has been killed is solely down to the whole area always being cordoned off between six and seven on competition day.

Arrows drizzle down onto the streets below like a feeble re-enactment of the battle of Agincourt.

Harry Holbroke curses as his first set of arrows all disappear off course. Thomas Potts does no better.

George Ferndill barges Margaret Featherstone aside and plants his feet behind the Narwal Line. He aims way to the left of the lamppost and shoots. For a second, the arrow seems destined for the lighthouse but the wind catches it and steers it back. It is the first arrow to head in anything like the direction of the hidden bandstand and target. Not having heard a word of Dunn's instructions, Ferndill fires his six arrows and carries on until three of the other competitors drag him away.

Another punch-up ensues as the men roll about on the lawn in front of a stoical Captain Cook up on his pedestal. He has seen worse.

Margaret takes advantage of the distraction to step up to the arch. She has seen the way the wind is blowing and watches with satisfaction as all six of her arrows disappear from view broadly in line with a point slightly to the left of where the bandstand must be.

And so it goes.

With three minutes to go everyone has discharged their arrows except for George Ferndill who took a right hook on the chin and is lying comatose on the grass. He wakes up, sees that everyone has finished, and screams he is being robbed. Leaping to his feet, Ferndill lurches to the Whalebone Arch and starts fast shooting his remaining forty arrows towards the harbour.

'Disqualified!' shouts Dunn after a minute, eyes on his fob watch.

Ferndill, still deaf as a doughball, continues shooting. 'I'll show you bastards!'

Dunn approaches Ferndill and shouts again, straight into his ear this time. Caught off-guard and fearing more sabotage, Ferndill spins round as he looses his arrow which flies straight into the ceremonial tricorne sealskin hat, whipping it off Dunn's head and sending it high into the air. It lands close by two juvenile herring gulls that splatter it copiously as they take flight.

In the hour that follows Ferndill is arrested, assistant Bovel is found hiding behind Cook's statue, a bucket of water is poured over Gordon to revive him, and it is determined that yet again no one has hit the target.

For the seventh consecutive year.

The closest arrow to the target is one of Margaret Featherstone's, found embedded in the bandstand roof, so she wins the Robin Hood Consolation Prize of a fish supper for two.

Twenty years later the BBC Home Service toys briefly with the creating a radio drama based around the competition. A pilot is recorded and aired, but concerns about public safety and the risk of copycat competitions sinks the idea. The reference to whaling is abandoned and The Whale Bone Archers is replaced with a gentler show set among country folk in the South West.

Whitby's Whale Bone Archery competition is consigned to the history books.

Endnotes - **How much of this is true?**

1 *The Flutter-Filch Stones*
There are various stones in the walls of the old town hall that resemble huge sandstone dice.

Hazard was a gambling game played with dice in the 18th century and fortunes were won and lost. 214 guineas is worth around £50,000 today.

King Henry III was given an elephant by the King of France in 1255 and a zoo was created at the Tower of London to house it, a polar bear and other animals.

2 *Swing Bridge Ghosts*
The new swing bridge was opened by Mabel Theresa Duncombe in July 1909. The history of the bridge is true.

The first Yorkshire car was the Bradford built Jowett 6.4 HP light car with a 816cc flat twin water-cooled engine.

3 *Dracula's Bootprint*
There is a left bootprint in concrete on Tate Hill Pier.

The *Demeter*, the ship that brought Dracula to Whitby, did end up on Tate Hill Sands in Stoker's tale.

4 Fakir's Door
The door of 37 Henrietta Street is studded with iron. Elizabeth I was petitioned to fund voyages to India and the British stayed 350 years and created the British Raj.

The earliest mention of a bed of nails is found in the Mahabharata, a Sanskrit epic poem.

5 *Teesside Tsunami*
People have taken donkey rides on Whitby beach for a long time, and the animals were led down Donkey Road from Abbey Field at the top of the cliff.

6 *Captains' Hooks*
A landslide in 1786 destroyed homes on Henrietta St.

Sailors were a very superstitious bunch and the superstitions listed are reportedly true. Touching a sailor's collar was thought to bring good luck.

Hooks do hang on a wall by No. 3 Sandgate.

7   *Phantom Chippy*
The world's first nuclear power plant was the Borax III, built near the small town of Arco in Idaho.

The AMI I 200 Vinyl jukebox, with selector wheel and spearmint trim did exist in 1956, as did the pink and brown 5 litre Mercury Montclair automobile.

And the French and the Belgians are still slugging it out as to who invented chips.

8   *The Smug Smugglers of Arguments Yard*
Smuggling was rife in old Whitby and up and down the coast. Harold Hutchinson was a customs officer and lived on Skinner Street. He had a reputation for corruption and ran a bordello.

The blubber boiling houses in Whitby stank to high heaven. Smugglers would take their goods up the ginnels and out onto the moors to hide them from view.

9   *Pavilion*
Whitby has a pavilion.

10 *Ballad of the Oak*
The press gangs were a blight in English ports. They kidnapped men and forced them to serve on Navy ships. Desertion rates and deaths were high and local people hated the gangs.

The riot in 1793 happened, as did the events in 1803 when the press gangs tried to seize the crew of *The Oak* as she sought safe harbour in a storm.

11 *Consummate Cook*
Captain Cook wrote a great deal about food in his journals.

He encouraged the ship's naturalists to find new plants to cook to prevent his crew getting scurvy.

12 *Reckless Lovers*
There are fossil designs in the concrete at the bottom of the path that leads to the east pier.

13 *Grand Day Out*
The Whitby to Pickering railway opened in 1836, seven years after Stephenson's Rocket won the prize. At the start, the carriages were made of converted stagecoaches bolted together and pulled by horses. It wasn't until 1845 that steam trains ran on the Whitby to Pickering line.

14 *Look Lively*
There are wonderful whale watching trips in Whitby.
    Oyston was captain of the *Mary*, a whaling ship. He and his crew witnessed the loss of the *Lively*, another whaler, in fierce gales in the Greenland seas in September 1826, as detailed in the story. All hands were lost.

15 *Festival Weekend*
Victorian men really wore pomade made from beef suet and lard. Dundreary whiskers were facial hair styles where the chin was left clean shaven. Mustachioed dandies were called whiskerandos.
    NB: John Flintoff is a ghost from 1900, visiting the Whitby Goth Weekend in 2021. Some of the weird gadgets he sees at the festival may now make sense!

16 *The Whale Bone Archers*
England won the Ashes in 1933 and Bing Crosby was a star. An Adeline Featherstone worked as a gardener in Whitby in 1829.
    The Inuit made hunting bows from whalebone. Whaling crews carved bone to stave off boredom on long voyages.

Everything else is nonsense!

Also by C.M. Vassie

SCRAVIR
While Whitby Sleeps

The explosive reimagining of Whitby's darkest hour!

The Famous Goth Weekend is in full swing. But while a mysterious guest star's music rocks the Pavilion, emaciated corpses are appearing in the streets. Dark forces are mingling with the thrill seekers.

Outsider Daniel Murray has never believed in the supernatural. Local girl Tiffany Harrek is not so sure. If they are to survive the next 48 hours they must wise up. Fast.

Readers' reviews of Scravir
"A dark brain-itching blend of gothic and contemporary"

"Brilliant. I was hooked & stayed in bed all day reading it."

"Intelligent, intense, packed with twists and genuinely original."

"An eerie brew of supernatural energy, antiquity and intrigue, Scravir is a real page-turner."

"Love this book ... absolutely fantastic, cannot wait for the next instalment."

"Wow! ... The only reason I put this book down was to go to work, decided to take the bus home so I could read uninterrupted for 50 minutes on the journey back ."

"I love anything dark & gothic that's set in Whitby .... Loved it ♥ "

Find out more at **www.injinipress.co.uk**